Termin

An inquiry into
violence in Norway

Published by Nordisk Books, 2019

www.nordiskbooks.com

Translated from *Termin,* copyright © 2016, Tiden Norsk Forlag
(All rights reserved)

This English translation copyright © Matt Bagguley, 2018.

This translation has been published with the financial support
of NORLA

Cover design © Nice to meet you

Printed and bound in Great Britain by Clays Ltd, Elcograf
S.p.A.

A CIP catalogue record for this book is
available from the British Library

ISBN 9780995485242

Henrik Nor-Hansen

Termin

An inquiry into
violence in Norway

Translated by Matt Bagguley

nordisk books

Also by Nordisk Books

Havoc
Tom Kristensen

You can't betray your best friend
and learn to sing at the same time
Kim Hiorthøy

Love/War
Ebba Witt-Brattström

Zero
Gine Cornelia Pedersen

In the early '90s Norway entered a period of long-term economic growth. Property prices rose. In Stavanger and Sandnes it became increasingly difficult to enter the housing market. Many young people looked to less expensive areas. Hommersåk was one of the surrounding villages which experienced an influx. The demography started to change. One could see a development of housing estates and infrastructure. It was known that growth in the oil industry would affect the society as a whole. A high level of activity propagated down to subcontractors and further into local business. There were considerable socio-economic ripple effects.

This inquiry looks at the case of Kjetil Tuestad, who in spring 1998 married Ann Elisabet Larsen. They had bought a house in Hommersåk. Kjetil was 26 years old. He worked as an electrician at Rosenberg Shipyard in Stavanger. On midsummer night of that same year he was found severely beaten on the outskirts of Hommersåk. Kjetil was unconscious when the doctor arrived. After a quick examination, he was transported by air ambulance to the emergency room at Stavanger University Hospital. They detected concussion, facial fractures, and breakages to the ribcage. Kjetil remained under observation for several hours. The head injuries were said to be serious. He regained consciousness the following morning.

Ann Elisabet Larsen says that her husband was found shortly before midnight. The police had obtained his personal details. Ann Elisabet then drove to the hospital in Stavanger. She says it was a long night in the waiting room. The information was supposedly inadequate. Finally she was allowed to go in and see him. At that point he was barely recognisable. His face was disfigured by bruising and swelling. She does not believe that Kjetil understood the situation. They said he was nauseous. Shortly afterwards he threw up. Ann Elisabet says she could not bear to be there. She later recalls being joined by Kjetil's parents in the waiting room. They had apparently requested to speak to the Duty Doctor. A man came out and informed them calmly of the damage to Kjetil's facial skeleton, with three of the fractures being in the jaw. There was extensive dental damage. Many teeth were bent in towards the palate. The parents were also told that their son had blood in his middle ear, which would impair his hearing. The outcome of the concussion was still uncertain.

Today Kjetil Tuestad says that he recalls little from this first period. Waking up was painful. He can remember developing an unusual headache. They had wheeled him down to the radiology department. The images had shown cerebral haemorrhaging. A surgical drain was considered. Kjetil thinks he perhaps lay in the corridor for a while. Later they may have taken him into a nearby room. Kjetil reportedly experienced a number of visual disturbances. It is known that he was concerned about the people around him. He says they tried to get into his oral cavity. Then he was left alone for a while. A doctor came and asked for his name and address. The doctor left.

The breakages to the jaw and right cheekbone were operated on. Kjetil was supposedly confused when he woke from the anaesthetic. He has no complete memory of this day. He says that it became dark. They had wheeled the bed over to the window of a six-patient room. During the night he was woken by lights and coughing. A nurse spoke quietly behind a curtain. Later, Kjetil reportedly called for help. It's unclear what he wanted. He lay for a while listening to heavy breathing and analgesia pumps. Kjetil thinks he may have slept. The next morning he was seen by a new nurse who had a wash-cloth and a nutritional drink. She explained to him about the jaw-brace. It would be six weeks before he could eat normally.

Kjetil Tuestad was bedridden for four days. He received no more news during the doctor's visits. He understood that, to a large degree, his body would heal itself. After a while the nurse placed a wheelchair by the bed. She removed his urinary catheter at the same time. Kjetil had to find the way to the toilet on his own. He says it was difficult to get in and out of the wheelchair. He had stabbing pains in his chest. At first, he also needed help getting onto the toilet seat. He explains how toilet visits could trigger discomfort and anxiety. His urine had smelled of penicillin. It was supposedly difficult to recognise himself in his own emotional life.

Kjetil Tuestad was admitted to the Neurosurgical Department at Stavanger University Hospital for two weeks. The parents had brought flowers and a box of chocolates. It was difficult to make conversation, he often sat in silence during visits. Over time he became gradually more indisposed. His wife says he seemed disoriented. He was not able to read books or newspapers. It is otherwise known that Kjetil avoided his fellow patients. He apparently experienced changes in his sleep pattern. He claims there was a lot of uncertainty surrounding his own future.

The investigation seemed to be low priority. Kjetil's family gradually lost hope. In late August the case got some renewed interest, when a six-year-old boy was almost stoned to death. An attempt had been made to spare the public, most of which never appreciated the seriousness of the offence. It was said that the boy's own peers had allegedly turned on him with kicks and punches. Eventually he was dragged into a ditch. He was later found in a very bad state, bleeding heavily. It was assumed that the boy would have permanent injuries. The stoning had taken place during the day, in a quiet residential area. People now believed that Hommersåk was losing its innocence. Sandnes Council reportedly involved the Health and Social Department. Various measures were considered. It was concluded that the children wanted to test their own reality. They had all just started school that year.

At first Kjetil Tuestad lived with the parents in Stavanger. Apparently he did not want visits from his wife. They spoke only rarely on the phone. These were said to be tiresome conversations which led nowhere. Kjetil recalls nothing of midsummer night, and nothing of the violence. He did not wish to talk about it. One could observe Kjetil's behaviour as a reaction. The mother took food, water and broth and then pulped everything in a Mixmaster. Kjetil did not eat enough. He lost a lot of weight. It is understood that he was often dizzy. His coordination failed, he needed help getting around the house. During this period Kjetil regularly visited the Department of Rehabilitation and Neuropsychology. They described the possibility of a reduced function in the central nervous system. He occasionally fainted throughout the summer. Once again he was admitted to the Neurosurgical Department. They said he was somewhat dehydrated. Otherwise, they found no real explanation. Kjetil Tuestad was kept there over the weekend. It was supposedly the end of the holidays at Stavanger University Hospital. Saturday morning he sat alone in the canteen, for a lengthy period. He was eventually joined by a woman with long greasy hair. They watched a documentary about reindeer. Kjetil experienced various aversions. He then wheeled himself down the corridor. He claims to have experienced a range of negative impressions. It is believed that the hospitalisation may have been a burden mentally. Kjetil remembers patients in red and blue dressing-gowns made of faded towelling. He had felt disoriented. He took the lift up several floors. It is believed that this may have been late Sunday evening. The departments were all in darkness.

Kjetil Tuestad had a new appointment in August. They removed the jaw-brace and made a few adjustments to the upper palate. A gradual improvement was seen in Kjetil's overall condition. He had been recommended further physical training. He apparently began taking daily walks using the walking frame. The mother followed him along the asphalt path by the residential area. Later, Kjetil was able to walk alone to the shop. He also used the walking frame to visit friends in the neighbourhood. They played computer games. Nevertheless it was easy to see that he felt dejected. Kjetil Tuestad failed to socialise in a meaningful manner. It was said that he was reserved and humourless. Cognitive tests continued to show memory loss around the time of the assault. There was reduced imaginative capability. Kjetil sometimes failed to understand his own life situation.[1] This had raised a few questions. The doctor wanted a new evaluation. However, there never was a new evaluation. The treatment ended in mid-August, when Kjetil returned for a check-up. The doctor had prescribed Apodorm for the sleep disorders. They talked briefly about the road ahead.

Rolf Tuestad was in regular telephone contact with Sandnes police station. They had rarely seen this kind of violence at Hommersåk. A lack of witnesses made the case difficult. It was crucial that people

[1]   On one of these occasions the father apparently called the outpatient clinic. A GP had spoken generally about post-traumatic stress disorders. No final response was provided.

came forward. The police believed that the Tuestad family should not have any high expectations. Cases like this often ended up being dropped.

Kjetil Tuestad reportedly moved to his own place in late August. It was a basement flat in Bjergsted. It is known that he called his parents and wife. He had apparently said that he needed time alone. They showed understanding. In hindsight, this approach has been questioned. The immediate family were perhaps not good enough at recognising changes in Kjetil's personality. He remembers very little from this period. In many respects he still required help. The flat never quite came together, there were pictures and cardboard boxes along the walls. The walking-chair occupied a lot of floor space. Kjetil was dependent on support points. He also had a walking frame, which is said to have stood on the gravel by the basement stairs. He used the walking frame to get to the nearest shop.

In September Kjetil Tuestad had several appointments with the dentist. He took the bus the short distance from Bjergsted towards Stavanger city-centre. The appointments involved a variety of cosmetic procedures. The chronic pain had supposedly lessened gradually during summer and autumn. Kjetil says he used fewer painkillers. Balance and coordination were nevertheless only slightly improved. Kjetil had been offered a physiotherapist, as well as rehabilitation training under the direction of the hospital. He apparently trained with stroke patients and those recovering from heart-surgery. Kjetil does not have much to say about it. People had lain on their own gym mat and kicked in the air. It was pure motoric training. After the session had finished it is understood that he used the walking frame to reach a nearby bus stop.

It appears that Kjetil Tuestad was mainly alone in the flat. He had problems concentrating. In his own words, the days just passed. It is known that he occasionally had the company of a white cat. He says the cat would come to the basement window. Kjetil recalls that he fed it liver paté. He believes it could have been the neighbour's cat. In October Kjetil was visited by his wife, Ann Elisabet Larsen. At first they had only spoken in the doorway. It is thought that she now understood that Kjetil had changed. She had expressed this to him. Kjetil's response was that he had recently taken a nap. They had apparently stared uncomprehendingly at each other. Kjetil asked if she wanted a coffee. Yes, thank you, she had answered. He then supported himself on the furniture for a while. He wanted to know if she took sugar. Ann Elisabet remembers that she laughed, a little nervously. Kjetil seemed unmoved. He took some sugar from the kitchen cabinet. It was unusual behaviour. Kjetil's speech was noticeably slower than before. His expressions were more monotone.

It is known that Kjetil Tuestad had thought a lot about the meeting with his wife. He recalls, above all, the difficulty of acting natural. He was afraid that she would notice this. They had drunk coffee at a low table in front of the TV. The TV was switched off, Kjetil recalls occasionally looking at the dark grey screen. Ann Elisabet wanted to know if he had contacted the Victim Compensation Office. He apparently confirmed that he would do so. Kjetil then supposedly looked at her.[2] He asked if she had become more involved in the local community. Ann Elisabet had reacted to her husband talking so strangely. 'More involved in the local community.' It is understood they sat for a long while in silence. In the end, Kjetil had asked if she wanted to watch TV. He stepped forward and turned on the TV.

Ann Elisabet Larsen now says that the conversation petered into insignificance. She was not able to persuade her husband to come home to Hommersåk. She felt that he needed more time alone. Kjetil recalls following her to the door. He assumed that they would never meet again. They supposedly gave each other a hug.

---

2   Kjetil Tuestad is unsure how his own facial expression was perceived. He feels today as though he stared.

Kjetil Tuestad spent Christmas with his parents in Madla. He ate turkey and opened presents. On Christmas Day it had begun to snow. He had helped to clear the driveway. It had got dark early. Kjetil had pushed a snow shovel, in long, slow stretches by the side of the house. Most of the snow ended up in the road. Kjetil talks about a distance, a kind of disconnection.[3] He turned towards the house and saw his father in the living room window. They acknowledged each other briefly.

3   A similar experience is seen Boxing Day, when the parents held a large coffee party at the house in Madla. Kjetil recalls an altered state of consciousness. He associates this change with loud voices in the hallway. They were relatives he had not met for a year and a half. Kjetil talks about a sense of derealisation when he gave the grandmother a hug. He also gave the aunt a hug and then shook hands with the grandfather and two uncles. They had all gone into the living room. The mother brought coffee. The conversation shifted to the snow out in the garden. Kjetil apparently sat in the background and cracked nuts. He was constantly aware of his own mechanical appearance.

It is known that Kjetil spent the Christmas week alone. He apparently played a lot of computer games. Kjetil says that Doom might seem primitive compared to today's video games. However he concedes that the game was addictive. It was difficult getting to sleep after the long sessions. His dreams often seemed troubled. Kjetil says he ate all meals in front of the screen. The meals usually consisted of two thick slices of bread, with jam and a large glass of milk. Kjetil says he did not eat much more than that. He rarely spent time making dinner. Practical things, like shopping for food, made him feel stressed. The period was marked by a certain cognitive dissonance.

On New Year's Eve, Kjetil Tuestad went out to meet people he knew in the nearby residential area. He used two folding walking-sticks. The walking-sticks had not worked so well on the slippery path. Shortly after, he felt unwell. He then lay down and rested in a dimly lit room with an unusually large number of teddy bears and pillows. After a while he sat at the edge of the bed. A plane flew overhead towards Stavanger airport. He had looked up at a poster of some horses. Kjetil could hear the New Year's Eve fireworks which occasionally broke through the music from the living room. He remembers the people becoming more rowdy. Some voices seemed uncontrolled, in the hallway just outside. Kjetil says that a couple of childhood friends had come in and joked around with him. He threw a small pillow about. It was all supposedly jovial. But Kjetil felt it was unlikely he would have much more to do with his friends. He was no longer the same. The feeling caused a great deal of discomfort, he does not think that alcohol could have altered his mood noticeably. After midnight, he went down to the main road alone. Once there he had apparently tried to hail a taxi. It had gradually begun to snow more, the water was noticeably dark in Hafrsfjord. Kjetil recalls that there was no wind. The snowflakes were large, it had snowed in a dead orange light. In the end he got a lift from two North African men. They drove him home for a certain fee. Kjetil remembers that the car rolled slowly over the snow-covered road. The men had spoken quietly in Arabic.

A snow-plough could be heard late in the evening on New Year's Day. It had snowed heavily in the early hours. Kjetil remembers that the snowy weather eased during the day, before beginning again in the evening. He had taken a bus to the parents to wish them a Happy New Year. The pine bushes were at the time partly covered with snow. The parents explain that it was unclear what mood Kjetil was in. They did not understand what was now stirring in the son. Kjetil had supposedly often said that he was happy, or that he ought to be happy.

During the spring, Kjetil Tuestad may have lost a little sympathy from those closest to him. He had been on sick-leave for almost a year. Kjetil had to make a decision about whether he would start claiming disability benefit or continue working as an electrician at Rosenberg Shipyard. At the time he wanted to take up social studies. It was explained that further studying would be difficult. During this period Kjetil had appeared a little helpless. He isolated himself from the family. It is understood that they had become concerned. A situation had developed where Kjetil Tuestad avoided all human contact. He had been going for long walks in his hometown Stavanger.[4]

4   Kjetil Tuestad says he always walked uphill towards Eiganes, and Eiganes cemetery. It was often misty. No wind. Some days, the park services are thought to have been working at the cemetery. Kjetil says he could hear hedge-trimmers across the whole neighbourhood. He passed through an area of wooden buildings and onwards down to the park. Two ducks sat out on the water. He remembers there being a number of hikers. Apparently he thought about suicide almost continuously. It was unusually warm for the time of year.

Kjetil says he had an impersonal relationship with himself. He claims to have felt a lot of emptiness and anxiety. In April he was admitted to the Division of Psychiatry at Stavanger University Hospital for two weeks. The parents had rung round the healthcare system. It was said that the son was clinically depressed.

Today Kjetil Tuestad can describe the meeting with the psychiatrist as positive. They looked closer at depersonalisation and other dissociative disorders. Kjetil was also able to talk to a psychologist. He was put on antidepressants. They gave him a room to himself, it is understood that Kjetil lay there flicking through Illustrated Science. From the window he could see the facade of the Child and Adolescent Psychiatry department. He says he drank some water. It had become cloudy. In the morning he was visited by a young male psychiatrist. Kjetil had been sleeping with his mouth open at the time. They had talked about identity.

Kjetil was seen to become more confident in the surroundings. It is known that he called his wife Ann Elisabet Larsen. He told her about the hospital admission. Ann Elisabet had replied that it was probably a good thing. He would now get help. But Kjetil recalls being indifferent to the conversation. Apparently he spent much of the day with a woman of the same age. They had sat in the canteen, and sometimes on the sofa at the end of the corridor. He calls her Britt Synnøve.

At first he thought that there could be something between them. They had both grown up in Madla. Britt Synnøve had spoken about personality disorders. Kjetil says a certain distance emerged at that point. He says they also had the company of other patients. But everything seemed vague, the medicine supposedly made him feel tired and under the weather. He claims it rained a lot in the last half of April. Below the window was a car park, and several rectangular green areas. Patients were as a rule silent, or chatted quietly and disinterestedly.

Kjetil Tuestad was discharged on Friday afternoon. He took a bus to the city centre and is known to have eaten dinner at a restaurant. He claims to have felt stressed by people in the room. Later, he apparently walked the streets. It is assumed that he stayed in the centre until the evening. Kjetil felt like he was being watched by people outside Stavanger Concert Hall. An elderly man had supposedly coughed and hawked in a furious manner. People had stood conspicuously silent in the foyer. Kjetil continued through Bjergsted and let himself into the bedsit. There were several missed calls on his phone. Kjetil spoke briefly with Ann Elisabet. He was asked about how it had gone at the hospital.[5] Kjetil told his wife that he needed to hang up. It is understood that he went to drink water from the tap. Kjetil says he had absolutely no idea what Ann Elisabet Larsen

5   Kjetil Tuestad remembers that during the telephone conversation he visualized the trees in Bjergsted as huge, dark illusions.

might have thought, or felt. Most surprising perhaps, was that all the suicidal thoughts returned. Kjetil apparently tried to relax by watching TV entertainment shows. He tried to laugh. At this point he believes that he reacted to his own laughter. He was supposedly afraid of acting out his own thoughts. It is known that Kjetil eventually called the Division of Psychiatry and spoke to the duty doctor. Kjetil was informed that the antidepressants could take somewhat longer to take effect. Kjetil says he had barely slept at all that night. He went into town at daybreak. Later he decided, on a whim, to go to the hairdresser. While there he was asked about how he wanted his hair.[6] Apparently Kjetil Tuestad did not answer this. He had then moved on to Finn's Patisserie where he stood in a queue for a while, and recalls there being people and umbrellas outside the window. For the next hour he walked around the pedestrianised streets, apparently feeling uncomfortable. It was Saturday shopping and a lot of people were in Stavanger city-centre.

---

6   Kjetil Tuestad says how he stood at the checkout later and saw tufts of his own hair on the floor. He also saw hair on the foot rest under the barber's chair. Snippets of hair had supposedly gathered in his lap and slid down the cape like dark flakes.

In the summer of 1999, Kjetil Tuestad supposedly
got to know a young woman in a wheelchair. He calls
her Anita. They had initially taken an elevator at the
Ullandhaug housing-blocks. Anita had then expressed
a wish to take her own life. She had apparently asked
if he could help her. Kjetil says he had not expected
anything like that, and that he had replied evasively.
Was the question meant to be taken seriously? Kjetil
says she had tried to laugh it off. He recalls that
they later spent time at an apartment in the centre
of Stavanger.[7] There they supposedly ate ice lollies
from the freezer box above the fridge. They had not
discussed anything worth mentioning. It is believed
that both may have felt shy. He recalls a situation
where Anita came out of the toilet, in her wheelchair,
with newly brushed hair. The hair is described as dry

---

7   Kjetil Tuestad describes two prosthetic legs which lay
on the sofa. The legs were simple aluminium tubes. He says that
he fetishised this a little. The feet had apparently been made of a
type of skin-coloured plastic or rubber.

and floating. She had laughed nervously, perhaps out of shyness.

It is now understood that the friendship was short-lived. It never evolved into a relationship. Kjetil remembers that they had been at the beach on two occasions. He had apparently carried her down to the water. There were some waves, they sat in the shallows both times. Anita talked about the traffic accident and how she had gradually accepted life in a wheelchair. Kjetil recalls how the waves constantly washed up onto the beach, water and foam had flowed all around, and he could feel the tiny sand particles brushing his skin. He says that he never dared to look directly at Anita's amputated leg. He found it bothersome and, according to him, the conversation had been entirely superficial. After a while he went off to urinate in a bunker from World War II. In hindsight, one could get the impression that there was a flat atmosphere. He says it was difficult to identify with his own words and actions. Kjetil now believes that the loneliness did something to him. It was difficult to think clearly. It is known that he took a long walk every night, most often around a nearby lake. Occasionally, he would follow the path to a more remote lake, which came out at the electricity substation, and then continued alongside a stream. He says it was a strange period. He had felt empty inside. In October the evenings were getting darker earlier, and he thinks they may have recently put the clocks back. The wind had dropped and it had become significantly colder. He describes long stretches of desolate footpaths. The trees lost their leaves, he could see a canopy of branches under the yellow-green lights of solitary lamp posts. He had been thinking a lot about a series of violent incidents in the late '70s, when several walkers were stabbed in the back. Nobody died of their injuries. Kjetil was just a young boy, he initially says he's unsure of the actual circumstances. He believes the police may have asked the public to be on the lookout for a male cyclist in his twenties. Kjetil says that the stabbings continued throughout the autumn of 1978, before the winter came and the weather turned bad. In all, five walkers had been stabbed in the back. The police believed that a small sharp instrument was used, perhaps a sheath knife. In most cases, the assailant had stabbed the victims on the left side, close to or in the left shoulder blade. In one case the knife had entered the lower back. A twelve-year-old girl was stabbed in the spring of 1979, she had suffered a punctured left lung. The final victim was a pensioner, in late October of the same year. All the victims were apparently taken to the emergency room with internal bleeding. The perpetrator was never caught. Kjetil says that even now one can feel that something could happen. It was supposedly easy to hear a bike on the gravel paths.

After the turn of the millennium, Sandnes came
out well in a survey about living conditions. The
municipal services covered a wide area. The
median income was above the national average and
households had greater purchasing power. Nevertheless, dissatisfaction was widespread. Local politics
had changed visibly. People became concerned
over transport and immigration. Commuters in
Hommersåk complained about traffic congestion at
Hana and on the main arteries in to Stavanger and
Sandnes. Many seemed receptive to a more polarised
and simplified depiction of the challenges faced by
society.

Kjetil Tuestad says that he moved back in with
his wife at Hommersåk. He says that it felt strange
and unfamiliar at first. He still believes they had an
almost normal life together. The summer and autumn
passed by quietly, with no significant incidents. Kjetil
is understood to have played a lot of computer games.
In October they had a baby, a little boy. Kjetil thinks
the child brought a change of content to the day.

He remembers a new, slightly sweet baby smell in the house. They had tried to look to the future, but Kjetil needed time to figure things out. He apparently explained to his wife that he wanted changes on a personal level. He made it clear that she too had to adjust. Kjetil had soon been receiving disability pay for a year and a half, he was now going to start reducing his antidepressants. There are indications that Kjetil tried to adapt to a new life situation.

At the start of 2001, they stuck to their New Year's resolution and went to Aqua-land. While there Kjetil experienced occasional bouts of drowsiness. He talks about an unusual distance to his surroundings. Sounds and visual impressions seemed far away. His wife had swum 1500 meters, while he had looked after the infant in a small, warm pool. After a while, Kjetil had apparently dozed off to sleep, and an elderly woman had woken him up. She had said that he should not be sleeping with a child in his arms. It's ok, he had answered. Kjetil says that he later took his wife and the children out to the parking lot. He remembers the air being strikingly cold. They drove to the Co-op and did some shopping. Then they continued to Hommersåk. Kjetil had long felt that something was not really as it should be. They had pulled up in front of the house. Kjetil says he must have carried the grocery bags to the door. He remembers having put a frozen pizza in the oven. He says that he went out on the veranda. The Ski World-Cup in Lahti was coming to an end. A number of crows had crossed the evening sky.

Kjetil now says it was difficult to play the father role. He has memories which feel alien to him. He believes that he was perhaps an entirely different person. Kjetil describes how he lay the baby on its stomach on the couch, its back and neck muscles were not yet fully developed. Apparently the baby was unable to lift its head up from the sofa. He remembers its breath, halting and strained. He says the child brought up a milky liquid, which supposedly stained the dark blue fabric. Easter had been spent with Petter Larsen, Ann Elisabet's father. It is known that the father-in-law picked them up unusually early.[8] Petter had then driven along Highway 45, well over the speed limit. Kjetil remembers that they did not stop to buy coffee. There had also been a discussion when Ann Elisabet needed to go to the toilet. In the end Petter had pulled off the highway towards a small wood. She had gone into the woods with a roll of toilet paper. In the end, the flow of Easter traffic turned out to be moving relatively fast. It took just an hour and a half to reach the cabin in Sirdalen. Kjetil

8   Kjetil Tuestad says he feels insecure in new situations, such as when meeting the father-in-law. Kjetil claims that he felt uncomfortable on the Easter road-trip itself, and also when skiing. He recalls an increase in depersonalisation leading up to it. One assumes that he may have distanced himself somewhat from the coming days on the mountain. Kjetil describes how his own voice sounded excessively loud and business-like when his wife helped him fasten the skis to the car-roof.

says the weather was quite poor, overcast and very windy. They spent most of the time indoors. He says the baby cried a lot. Petter had become very drunk on Maundy Thursday, and was apparently unpleasant towards the daughter. On Good Friday they could see snow drifts building up along the wall of the cabin. On Easter Saturday they had eaten lamb. On Easter Sunday there had been occasional sunny periods, but it was still windy.

Kjetil Tuestad says that they rarely spoke about the assault. Nor was he, at the time, particularly troubled by thoughts of revenge. It is assumed that there was a great deal about the assault that he did not understand. Kjetil says he was unable to grasp the violence. He tried going for walks in the neighbourhood. This was also in line with recommendations that had been made. In the evenings he walked around Riska Secondary School and beyond, down through the housing estate. The family had looked upon this as a process, however it is known that the walks provided vague, slightly blurred impressions. Kjetil remembers tyre tracks in the soft snow. He hardly ever saw anyone. He recalls fully lit houses, yet there were no people.

Warnings had been given about situations that might trigger fear and aggression. Now that notion would need to be reconsidered to a degree. The impression one got from Hommersåk was far more static. The demographics were changing, many local people believed they recognised themselves in what

35

was then called 'Stavanger-syndrome.' Neighbours had stopped greeting each other. People could appear taciturn and evasive. It was said that they only saw one another in their cars. Long-term economic growth seemed to have forced out a different, more measured form of social exchange. It is known that many people hid behind the facade of a busy day. Nevertheless, it was hard to see any real alternative. Hommersåk was no longer sheltered. The express ferry to central Stavanger had been improved. Road traffic had also increased. Driving times to Sandnes, and beyond to the big chain stores at Forus, had been reduced.

During the holidays in 2001, two people were subjected to brutal violence at a psychiatric unit for drug addicts. Both were flown to Stavanger University Hospital. One had a skull fracture and later died from the injuries. The local newspaper wrote that politicians had been cutting back on the psychological help programme currently available for drug rehabilitation. Kjetil does not think he reacted to the incident especially. He says he perhaps lacked empathy for drug addicts. It had also been extremely warm. They had apparently gone on a trip to a shopping centre at Forus. Kjetil says that his wife had wanted to buy a highchair. In reality, she went into a variety of shops. They had then eaten meatballs at IKEA.

Between 2002-04 a number of broadband ditches were dug at Hommersåk. A few years later, social media began to interfere in people's lives. A change was seen in human relationships. In Hommersåk it was believed that the internet had reduced the distance to the more central parts of the region. This was in any case an unintended effect, that would increase significantly over the next decade. At the same time, the school services reported an increasingly sexualised climate among teenagers. The development was troubling. At Riska Secondary School, a letter was drafted expressing concern about widespread self-aggrandisement on the aforementioned media. A new and very distinctive form of narcissism was seen to emerge. Most youngsters had unrealistic, often completely distorted ambitions.

Following Easter 2009, an unusually large number of pupils began dropping out of lessons. It was said to have been miserable weather at the time, with sleet clouds over Hommersåk. People spent most of the time indoors. At Riska Secondary

School, teachers reported concentration difficulties and widespread apathy. Absences reached unacceptable levels. There was fear of an even further decline amongst the pupils. The school counsellor requested meetings, where many pupils expressed that the teaching did not feel relevant. The problem was traced partly to a LAN party in Eastern Norway, where the boys at least had played computer games for several days. Parents' meetings were held. The high absence rate continued throughout the spring and summer. Rogaland Municipality eventually became involved. Many wondered if Hommersåk might have distinct needs. The population was approaching 6000.

In Stavanger and the surrounding area, there had been a noticeable split in the labor market for some time. The petroleum industry had driven wages and prices up. One could question this development. At the same time it was clear that the economic upswing resulted in continuous building in peripheral areas. Hommersåk had long seen an increase in families with young children and new homeowners. An overwhelming majority said they were motivated by low land prices. Secondary was the proximity to nature and suitable hiking areas nearby. It was nevertheless observed that outdoor activities were in decline. There was extensive commuting and car use. Parents with toddlers often displayed signs of having stress-related illnesses. Many suffered from undefined afflictions. No immediate reasons were found as to why Hommersåk should be burdened.

Further surveys revealed a widespread obesity problem among the younger generation. This corresponded with nationwide developments. A high level of sugar consumption, in the form of sweets and sugary drinks, was confirmed. Ready meals were widely used. Most eye-opening perhaps was the spread of fear and aggression. Readings showed very high room temperatures. Poor ventilation had resulted in increased cases of mites and allergies. Many pensioners displayed signs of sleeping badly at night. Enlarged prostates and nightly urination was a problem among men. Some also complained about Silicosis, after having inhaled cement dust from nearby industrial areas.

Kjetil Tuestad stresses that he is only occasionally able to picture his wife in the home. He says it is also difficult to visualise the infant, as he would have looked in the summer of 2001. Kjetil reacts to the fact that he did not participate more often in this. Other memories well up quite clearly. During the holidays, what would become a string of severe animal welfare cases began. Cats in particular were made to suffer.[9] Kjetil also recalls having used a high-pressure hose on his own house. He can picture water and paint flakes being blasted away from the walls and windows. Kjetil describes the extensive job of painting the house white. He had a two-piece aluminium ladder that extended all the way up to the roof ridge. During the

9   The local newspaper wrote about cats which had been found taped to lamp posts. The police also confirmed that the cats were soaked in flammable liquids and then set alight. The public had been asked for tips on the matter. Over the summer cats began showing up with their paws cut off. In August school pupils found a pregnant cat in the grass behind Riska Secondary School. The police reported that there were twigs stuck in the cat's reproductive and rectal orifices.

summer, his thoughts became more uncontrolled. It is understood that Kjetil had been thinking a great deal about the assault in 1998. He began to think that one, or several, of the perpetrators were in his immediate vicinity. He had therefore reacted more aggressively on a number of occasions.

Kjetil Tuestad says he saw the need for greater intimacy with his wife. Today he realizes this need was bombarded by other, more unclear impressions.[10] He can see himself becoming quickly restless and irritated. He perceives his own memories as severely fragmented. A cement mixer was turning nearby. He also believes he could hear nail guns. He says the paint tin hung on the ladder from a S-shaped hook. It is believed to have rained a lot in August. Kjetil remembers taking down the ladder and laying it beside the garage wall. Then he had supposedly put the brushes in a canning jar with some paint thinner.

It is known that Kjetil Tuestad felt inauthentic when dealing with children. He can recall mornings sitting beside the cot, pulling faces so that the son might smile or laugh. Kjetil could often become very self-conscious. He believes children can tell if an adult is present as a person. But there were also other aspects of being a father. Kjetil recalls how some nights he carried the son carefully around the house.

10   Kjetil Tuestad apparently downloaded a fair amount of pornographic material. He does not believe there was any sex life after the birth. Kjetil admits that he would often resort to masturbation when something felt difficult.

So much of the child felt close, like the shoulder region and the chubby infant limbs.

In August 2002 several motorists reported a naked
girl on Highway 516. It is known that she went into
a nearby wood after a while. The police arrived later.
The girl had become extremely cold. They drove her
to the rape referral centre in Stavanger. A forensic
examination was carried out. The girl was said to be
in shock. She needed help getting dressed. Medical
personnel found vaginal tearing and several burn
marks on her body. There were also other marks, of
a then unknown character. The police linked the
case to a domestic disturbance in Eskemyrveien.
A number of youths had been partying there all
weekend. The sixteen year old girl had supposedly
been locked inside since the Friday night. On the
Saturday night, several of the boys had come in and
raped her, one by one. It is believed girlfriends also
took part. The youths fired air guns as the girl was
forced to urinate on the lawn. All those involved
resided in Hommersåk and attended Riska Secondary
School. The girl was eventually transferred to Kannik
Secondary School in Stavanger. She was often absent.

Her grades were consistently weak. Towards the end
of October, she completely avoided lessons. Over
the next few days the girl apparently spent a lot
of time in Stavanger city centre. She was arrested
for theft at H&M. They said she had been stealing
knickers. The mother had then contacted the girl's
biological father in Stockholm, they wanted to try a
change of environment. From mid-November the
girl lived with her father, in a three-room apartment
in Rådmansgatan. The father reported early on
that the daughter's hair was unkempt and that she
rarely washed. It is understood that she watched a
lot of television. One evening in December the girl
left the apartment and went out into the snow. The
father thinks she may have followed the route of
the E20. During the morning she was observed at
Karolinska University Hospital and what was then the
Institute for Radiological Protection. The police got
hold of her. Christmas was spent with the mother in
Hommersåk. It had rained quite a lot. The girl would
not step outside the front door. On Boxing day, she
came into the care of Sandnes District Psychiatric
Center, in Varatun. She was admitted after disfiguring
her own face with a razor blade. Photographs show
vertical cuts down both cheeks. There were also
a large number of transverse cuts across the left
forearm. She reportedly bled all over the bedding and
mattress. The risk of further self-harm was considered
relatively high. The girl responded badly to anti-

depressants. Compulsory mental health care was recommended.

The principle had held a series of meetings with the teachers at Riska Secondary School. Initially, answers were sought for what could have been done differently. Then a plenary meeting was held with the pupils and their respective parents. One father had stood up and asked if it was really possible to love children who raped. There was a lot of input. Several parents demanded stronger measures be taken.

In May 2003 Hommersåk Outdoor Nursery had a gathering in a nearby forest. Kjetil Tuestad says he drove there together with two of the other fathers. He says it was unclear what was happening. After a while they had turned off the main road. Kjetil remembers they drove aggressively into Svilandskogen. They took a sharp right turn, up a straight gravel track. There were many cars parked between the trees. Kjetil and the other two fathers are thought to have parked, and then followed a path into the forest. They had to walk for a while before Kjetil was given any idea of what was supposed to happen. A number of women stood waiting. People shook hands with each other. Kjetil says it seemed remarkably formal. He believes most of them could have been mothers from the neighbour-hood. The kindergarten staff were presumably there as well. Several of those in attendance were dressed like Indians. It was explained that the kids were gathered down in the camp. Kjetil was wearing a bear

mask which apparently had a strong smell. The plan
was that Kjetil would simply go down to the kids and
'scare the living shit out of them'. It is now known that
those in attendance walked together down a steep
slope. Kjetil says that the kids ran away as soon as
they saw him. Some appeared to be of early school
age, so they seemed a little older than anticipated. He
apparently didn't hear the kids screaming or crying.
Kjetil remembers that he ran until he was sweating,
it was birch forest and quite hilly terrain. Several of
the dads had complained about being in bad shape.
Kjetil says that something felt wrong. It was something
he had thought about at least. The bear mask had
become hot and uncomfortable. He had eventually
got separated from the others. The children had
hidden themselves, or had possibly run away. Kjetil
claims that he walked around a marsh, and then
entered a dense thicket. He says he was unsure of his
own role.

    The treatment of the children was reported
to the police. In Hommersåk it became gradually
accepted that a serious assault had taken place within
the local community. Those involved struggled to
explain what had actually happened. The case
increased in magnitude. Hommersåk Outdoor
Nursery was found to have several areas worthy of
criticism. Employees felt that the work environment
and pay conditions may have given some an excuse
to sabotage their own guidelines. Many children were

said to be demanding, at times hyperactive. There were also disagreements among the parents.

Sandnes police station reportedly continued its investigation throughout the autumn. One young woman testified how she, as a new mother, had been affected by the local mothers' group. She claimed that mothers regularly performed the so-called 'still face' experiment. Nobody was allowed to comfort a crying infant. A distinct group dynamic had gradually broken down those involved. Several mothers later came forward and said that it became difficult to express any objections, they felt completely unable to set limits. It was noticed that many suffered psychological reactions. Hommersåk became the focus of rumour and suspicion. The police therefore went out and asked the public to wait for a further assessment. Legal repercussions were expected but no claims were made.

Kjetil Tuestad says he can close his eyes and see a man on the highway. It is snowing. Houses and buildings appear monotonous. The man crosses the car park in front of the chemist. He opens the door and walks in. He can hear that the voice is monotonous too. It is a clear recollection. At the same time, the recollection feels unclear. He senses a distance. 'I'm popping out to the chemist.'

In the winter of 2011 Kjetil Tuestad was introduced to Narrative Exposure Therapy. He was alone in life at this point. At the Division of Psychiatry, it was believed that Kjetil lacked confidence in his own community. Kjetil says that prior to being admitted, he had experienced a long period of anxiety. He worked at Skretting in Hillevåg at the time, where he apparently packed fish feed, and also helped with its distribution. It is understood that Kjetil Tuestad got on quite badly with several employees. Many lived in Hommersåk or had backgrounds from there. After a while the conflict led to a partial sick leave. Kjetil is said to have discussed the situation with the

51

HR manager, who remarked that suicidal thoughts in themselves were not so unusual. Some reassignments were made nevertheless. Kjetil was assigned to installing new computer equipment. He also installed new software. In December the conflict led to a scuffle. A Christmas party had been organised by the company and during the evening Kjetil Tuestad had apparently clashed with two men. Kjetil had punched one of them in the face and he had received a blow to the eye himself. They had supposedly pushed each other around on the gravel outside the venue. Kjetil lost some shirt buttons and his new moccasins got trodden on. He had then gone into the toilet. He needed to put toilet paper in his nostrils. Spots of blood had landed on his shirt. Kjetil recalls leaving the venue and going up to the main road. Later he caught a bus back to his own house, which at that time was a loft apartment on Hillevågsveien. It is known that Kjetil felt uncomfortable with his own thought patterns. Sunday morning he took a cab to the Division of Psychiatry at Stavanger University Hospital. Kjetil was put on anti-anxiety medicine and given a room facing the Hillevåg tunnel. It is not thought that he notified any relatives. It is known that he slept a lot in the afternoon and evening. He lay sleepless that night. He switched on the lights above the bed. Kjetil remembers that he pulled the sheets aside and exposed the mattress, which seemed to be brand new. At dawn it had rained against the window. A number of seagulls stood motionless on the grass below.

Ann Elisabet Larsen requested a separation in December 2002. Kjetil admits to being at a loss over how he should react. A number of practical problems had apparently cropped up. First of all, he had to find a new place to live. The rental market was difficult. He had to live with the parents in Stavanger for a while. Eventually he moved in with Astrid Tuestad, his own grandmother. Kjetil remembers that she had been very ill, with a weak heart. She was transferred to the nursing home at Tasta where she also contracted double pneumonia. The strain is thought to have changed her. Kjetil recalls one snowy winter day when Astrid returned from the nursing home in a minibus. She had seemed frail. Kjetil supported her on the steps up to the house. Kjetil says he was not even sure if she recognised him. He had explained in a loud voice that he was Kjetil, son of Rolf, who was her son. She complained that it was so cold in the living room. Later she spent an unusually long time in the bathroom. Kjetil says that toiletries fell from the shelf under the mirror. A deodorant had rolled around in the sink.

Kjetil admits that he never had much of a connection with his 85-year-old grandmother. They had tried to chat. She had sometimes talked about the war. Kjetil says the grandmother recalled many striking details, such as Germans torturing the school principal with electric shocks to the penis and testicles. He had no idea if Astrid was telling the truth. In the evenings she always took out a large plastic box of ginger biscuits, sometimes she also made waffles. Kjetil says that the conversation sometimes felt strained, partly off topic, he would most often sit with a laptop on his knees. The TV would also be on.

There are images and notions. It is understood that Kjetil took a walk early one morning in January. He talks about a cold dawn. He had walked to the park. He can picture crows in the naked treetops. There had apparently been ice on the lake. Some children threw stones, Kjetil says he can hear the stones bouncing across the icy surface. He claims that detailed memories always make him a little uncomfortable.

Astrid Tuestad is known to have passed away a few months later. It would seem that she felt poorly after dinner. Kjetil had taken her to the emergency room. There was a long queue. Astrid preferred to go home and rest. Kjetil says he drove her back to the house at Byhaugen. This was Friday, June 22, 2003. Kjetil says he sat drinking beer until half past ten in the evening. After that he was ready to go out on the town. He recalls coming into the living room intoxicated. He supposedly reacted to the fact that the TV was off, he had gone and knocked on Astrid's door. It is known that he then became aware of his grandmother's death. One would expect a natural display of grief. Instead Kjetil apparently put his shoes on. The weather was nice and there were lots of people in Stavanger city centre. Kjetil Tuestad went to several bars. Kjetil claims that he had a feeling that anything could happen. However, it does not seem that anything significant did happen. He spent the night at a disco where according to him he stood and stared at people dancing. On his way home he went to a 24-hour petrol station and bought two hot-dogs. He had now forgotten about his deceased grandmother. Kjetil does not recall thinking about Astrid until after he had gone to bed. He then went naked down to her room on the ground floor. It would seem that he felt a little shy, he allegedly went and put on some clothes, he mentions shirt and underpants. It appeared as though Astrid had moved. Kjetil says she lay facing the door, he thought she had watched as he entered. He had stopped a short distance from the bed. He then realised she was just staring unfocussed into space. Kjetil says he was unsure whether this was real, he was evidently very intoxicated. Kjetil describes how he sat on the edge of the bed and held her hand. The wrist and elbow had a certain stiffness, the arm did not move normally.

It is believed Kjetil Tuestad attempted to write about the break-up of his relationship. He probably did not handle the break-up so well. After his grandmother's passing, he had found a basement flat in Hommersåk, not too far from his ex-wife. An agreement had been reached where Kjetil could pick up the child from kindergarten on certain days. He says that the son was now almost three years old. The son cried in the beginning, Kjetil had crouched down and asked, while laughing, if he was afraid of his own dad. He jiggled the boy around a little.

Kjetil Tuestad is understood to have spent time with the couple on the floor above, especially with Stian, who was only one year younger than him. They had two small children. Kjetil says that in late autumn he was invited to watch an international match against Spain, where Norway lost 0-3 at Ullevaal Stadium. Stian had responded emotionally. He supposedly kicked holes in two cupboard doors in the bathroom. Kjetil explains that he too felt affected, swept along by it all possibly. It was the last chance to reach the knockout phase of the European Championship.

Shortly before Christmas, Kjetil Tuestad began as a stand-in caretaker at Riska Residential and Activity Center. The position was never formally advertised. Kjetil says he began at short notice, because of illness. It was allegedly Stian who fixed him the job. Kjetil describes the center as a mustard-yellow wooden building, not far from Riska church. It had apparently been five years since he had last taken part in any work. The position lasted for three months, during winter 2003-2004. Kjetil says that the main duties were related to maintaining central heating equipment, and ensuring that other facilities worked as prescribed. Otherwise there was a lot of sporadic work. Kjetil believes the subconscious sorted out new information, he apparently experienced many realistic dreams during the period.

It is known that Kjetil Tuestad worked among the elderly and those in need of care. He met people who were in the final stages of life. There were old ladies who supposedly bore a striking resemblance to his own deceased grandmother. Kjetil found some of the pensioners whiney, they always let him know if he wasn't on time, or if he ever broke his own promises.

It snowed heavily over the New Year's weekend. Kjetil remembers a snowplough clearing the badly-lit car park. He too had to clear snow from a couple of emergency escapes. He apparently walked at the back of the building, under the light from the large canteen windows. The snow had blanketed the area, and it was difficult to get an impression of the surroundings. A man had come along and said that he was unhappy, it was too hot in his room, among other things. They had stood chatting in the snow. The man talked about his time in the Home Guard, where he had been a sergeant. The winters were colder then. There had been a lot of snow in the mountains. The man told him that twelve soldiers had been lost in the area, a huge search party had been sent out. Several avalanches were thought to have occurred in the area. A new search commenced in the spring thaw of 1965. A few remains were found, such as shoes and wool-hats. Kjetil was unsure whether the man was telling the truth. He recalls the silence when the man went back inside. Except for a single tractor, somewhere beyond the snow-capped firs.

Between Christmas and New Year the weather was mild and rainy. The snow melted in a few days. Kjetil remembers the darkness at this time, he thinks that might be why he dreamt so much. Kjetil says he replaced fluorescent lamps in the dementia ward. He had a sense of being observed, it felt strange to move around on the step-ladders. Kjetil recalls spending a while removing the grid from the light fitting. He apparently said to himself that the demented didn't understand. It was dark when he went home in the afternoon. He thinks the winter darkness had some meaning.

Kjetil Tuestad expresses difficulties with acting in a social context, such as while working at Riska Residential and Activity Center. He considers himself inarticulate when encountering other people. He says that something gets lost. He attended a Christmas dinner, where it had sometimes felt difficult to assume the role of a private person. It is understood he danced with a nurse until late in the evening, she told him that some of those with dementia could show signs of a heightened sex drive. There were men who had masturbated in the sitting room. Many were real bastards, they could be verbally abusive to the staff. Kjetil recalls that the nurse had seemed drunk. They had supposedly walked along the high street in Sandnes. He says it was unclear what she really wanted.

Kjetil Tuestad admits having thought less and less about his wife and child. He says there was nothing there for him. He considered the work mentally demanding, often it felt like it was enough with TV and the internet. Kjetil nevertheless thought that he wasn't able to be a good enough father. At weekends he could also feel a little bit alone. Stian had invited him to join Hommersåk Basketball Club. Kjetil recalls having walked to Riska Sports Hall in the rain. The hall appeared to be closed at the time. Later the rain stopped, he had gone down to the main road and on towards Hommersåk town centre. Kjetil says that he passed a number of youths who were allegedly smoking beside a black Honda. It is possible they shouted some abuse. Kjetil admits that he pretended not to hear. He is unsure if he should have reacted, and if so how. He continued up Breivikveien. For the next few evenings he is thought to have played a lot of computer games. Further exposure therapy may have been worth while.

Kjetil Tuestad has tried to put his friendship with Stian into words. He says that Stian had worked on a North Sea oil platform at the time, with four weeks off between every two week shift. They had apparently found some common interests. In March his job at Riska Residential and Activity Center had also come to an end. Kjetil says they played computer games. In April they had fished from the rocks at Ulsneset. There was a distance, it seems they had never really confided in each other. Kjetil had mentioned the assault, and was surprised that Stian had not heard of the case. Stian was also surprised. He appeared to have difficulty believing that such a thing could happen in Hommersåk, completely unprovoked. There were differences of opinion on this. Kjetil believes that Stian's statement was a projection of their wider friendship. He said they also stood a good distance apart physically. Stian had caught a lot of Ballan wrasse.[11] Kjetil recalls catching a one-and-a-half kilo cod. He had gutted it in the bay, where the water was painfully cold as he crouched

11   The lure often got stuck in the bony throat. It is believed that Stian tore out the hook and threw the Ballan wrasse at the sea. A few fish floated on the surface.

and rinsed the fish by the shore. He could see
Stavanger on the other side of the fjord. Kjetil says it
was overcast and windless. He threw the guts into the
water.

It has been confirmed that Stian had a
small boat with a 4 HP outboard motor. During the
holidays they supposedly did a lot of trolling in the sea
near Usken. Kjetil says that they occasionally smoked
marijuana. It is believed that the narcotic substance
may have triggered a dissociative anxiety disorder.
Kjetil describes an uneasiness. He says he saw fish
moving about in the clear water. They had moored on
the east side of Usken, where Stian built a campfire.
Kjetil then experienced a number of aversions to his
friend. He became worried about acting impulsively.[12]
It is understood that he alleviated this by walking
around the cabins on the island. Kjetil says that he
saw women sunbathing. He had walked beneath a
large terrace where it was apparently possible to see
the outlines of beach mats. Kjetil describes a situation
where he sat out of sight and masturbated. He is
thought to have wiped the sperm from his hand on
some nearby planks.

---

12   Kjetil Tuestad has acknowledged occasionally fearing
his own violent fantasies. At Usken, he had felt the urge to smash
the back of Stian's head in with a rock. Thoughts such as these
are described as fleeting.

During autumn 2009, Kjetil Tuestad worked at the patient hotel at Stavanger University Hospital. He apparently helped with serving breakfast and lunch. In December he began a short friendship with Sofia, who had just been transferred from the Gastric Surgery Department. They sat in the cafe and drank tea or coffee. Sofia had a Polish background. The family had fled Poland in the early '80s. She had been suffering from Crohn's disease for a couple of years, and they had now removed the large intestine. Six weeks later, she was still struggling with post-operative infections. Not much else is known about Sofia. She lived on the first floor, in a small room with a single bed and TV. Kjetil says there were skin-coloured colostomy bags under the TV bench. A red cardigan hung over the chair. Otherwise, it seems there were few or no personal belongings in there.

Kjetil Tuestad clearly remembers the silence at the patient hotel. He cannot recall there ever being laughter or a raucous conversation. He describes Sofia as somewhat younger than him, perhaps in her

early twenties. They lay cramped on the narrow bed.
Kjetil says he sometimes felt repulsed by her. He had a
feeling that this was unkind. Her stomach and breasts
smelled faintly of antiseptic. Kjetil says he could
feel stiff pubic hair. Afterwards he lay motionless
for a while. Today he believes that the situation was
not sexually related. It had started to snow. He saw
snowflakes above the grey concrete parking-facility.
Kjetil says he found the patient hotel oppressive and
totally free of acoustics. He assumes the building was
thoroughly soundproofed. The silence could give
the impression it was deserted. Kjetil recalls Asian
women going from room to room with cleaning carts.
They often seemed withdrawn and sad. He rarely saw
people on the second floor. He describes corridors
with fitted carpets in a dark alternating pattern. Kjetil
believes something may have changed within him.
The work seemed heavier, finding the motivation
got worse. It is assumed that the period was marked
by certain mental disorders. In the cafe he saw
young couples wheeling premature babies around.
He remembers tiny premature faces with almost
flame-red skin, in transparent cots made of glass or
plastic.

In spring 2010, Stavanger and the surrounding
area once again became the focus of animal abuse.
In Hommersåk, a dog was found in the sea, weighed
down with a stone. The local newspaper wrote that
its legs had been tied and it had been decapitated. In
Stavanger, some little boys had beaten a hedgehog

with sticks before dousing the animal in petrol and setting it alight. Just a few days later, a total of six ducks and ducklings were tortured to death near a secondary school in Jæren. Passive witnesses had filmed while fellow students tore off the heads and wings. Kjetil Tuestad is convinced that events like this had an impact. During this period he had supposedly thought very negatively about humanity and human beings. The summer was cold and windy, it had rained a great deal in Western Norway. Kjetil often sat indoors playing online computer games. It had also rained when he was invited to a party at Stian's. A number of party-guests are thought to have become highly intoxicated. Some became rowdy as they grilled sausages under the porch roof. Kjetil says children were present too. He thinks the children may have perceived the adults' world as unsafe.

Kjetil Tuestad was discharged from the Division of
Psychiatry in April 2012, after a two month stay. It is
understood that he walked home to Hillevåg in nice
spring weather. The bedsit was supposedly overheated.
Kjetil says the radiators were still on full. At this point
he had felt a sudden distance to his own life. The bed
sheets appeared to be covered in large stains. Kjetil
says he did not want to be that kind of person. He
had lain directly on the floor, by the window facing
the main road. He remembers metallic clanging
noises from the radiators, which must have then been
cooling gradually. It is not known if the medication
was to blame for the tiredness. Kjetil says he lay on
the floor for a while. He could feel the vibrations from
buses and larger vehicles.

      It is known that Kjetil Tuestad continued as
a day patient at the Division of Psychiatry. No final
diagnosis was given. He described a greater density
in his own daily life, as well as in his experience of
it. He did not socialise noticeably with others in the
department. When Kjetil turned 40, the staff served

a little sponge-cake. He recalls that he was genuinely surprised. At this point he praises the psychiatric staff. Later it is thought he took the bus downtown and went to the shopping centre. It is understood that he sat in a cafe. After that he had bought a doughnut and walked to the escalator. He went up a few floors. There were lots of people. Kjetil says he felt a number of aversions towards immigrants, especially Muslim men. He does not recall ever reacting to dark-skinned people before.

On the 17th of May, Kjetil Tuestad says he stood for a long time in Cathedral Square. It had rained. He supposedly ate a hot-dog outside the bank. Kjetil believes it was late in the afternoon, he had watched a lot of people returning from the Constitution Day parade. Kjetil then apparently walked alongside Stavanger Cathedral and down to the city park where he got chatting to an older alcoholic man. They had talked about football, and how the local team Viking had a chance of winning the league that year. Kjetil says he and the man left the park together. He clearly remembers the gravel crunching under his hard, patent leather shoes. They had walked up Breibakken. Otherwise Kjetil has no idea what streets they may have followed through the neighbourhood. They had walked down into east Stavanger. The apartment is said to have been on the ground floor of a two-storey wooden house. The entrance apparently smelled of cat piss. Kjetil recalls a lot of cats on the stairs and on the windowsill. He says that he continually felt subject to the will of the older man. Kjetil describes a feeling of unease. They had drunk liquor from a five-litre container of home-made spirits. The man reclined on the couch, he is thought to have been extremely intoxicated. Two kittens climbed on the sofa. Kjetil says it was impossible to have a conversation. He could not make out anything other than nonsense. Kjetil says he stood up and hit the man several times with an empty wine bottle. He remembers that the man remained lying in the same position. Kjetil had at first thought the blows had been ineffective. The first one had been a little clumsy, the bottle had glanced the man's ear and struck his collar bone. The next blows landed right on his crown. Kjetil says it took several hard cracks before the bottle shattered. He was left holding the bottleneck and spout. Fresh blood is said to have poured from the man's hair. Kjetil claims he could see blood running down his temples and cheeks. He had then gone to the toilet. Kjetil supposedly urinated in what he describes as unhygienic conditions. After that he left the apartment. Kjetil says he stopped at the Shell petrol-station in Pedersgata. He bought an ice cream. He cannot remember being in touch with his own emotions. It is assumed that he continued along Pedersgata. He thinks the Constitution Day Parade had finished, people began to move from the city streets. Kjetil does not remember clearly. He says that night fell. He describes how a street sweeper slowly drove across the square.

Kjetil Tuestad says he went back to the man. The man apparently stood there frying eggs, bare-chested. It has emerged that Kjetil had walked straight in. They stared incredulously at each other. The man held a spatula in his hand. He still seemed drunk. The fried-eggs were presumably cooking on far too much heat, and spat furiously in the frying-pan. He told Kjetil that he was not welcome. Kjetil says he did not answer. He could see congealed blood in the man's hair. This became evident when the man sat down to eat at the table. He had ignored Kjetil's presence to some extent. A cut on his scalp was still bleeding, it was an open wound. Kjetil says that he suggested a trip to the emergency room. Maybe they would have to give him some stitches. But the man did not want to see a doctor. He complained of head pains.

Kjetil Tuestad says he was in the apartment until gone midnight. There was hardened blood on areas of the floor and furniture. Kjetil helped the roughly sixty-year-old man into bed. The man was dizzy, he had thrown up in the bathroom and was spluttering heavily. Kjetil supposedly tucked the duvet around him. At this point the man complained about pain in his collar bone. Kjetil assumes that the man had a breakage, possibly a fracture. He describes a bruise with some swelling. The man drew his hand slowly up to the injury. It hurts here, he is believed to have said. Kjetil gave no reply to this. He sat by the man's bed. A cat had jumped up onto his lap.

Kjetil stroked the cat. He remembers empty bottles and two brown bananas on the windowsill. The harbour silo rose high above the nearby rooftops. It was dark outside, except for some stray light from the street-lamps.

Various treatments were used at the Division of Psychiatry. They had occasionally confronted Kjetil with the objects of his anxiety. He responded well to Imaginal Exposure Therapy, and seemed able to put some of his ideas into words. It is understood that he had a partner between 2012-14. He says that they lived in Vardeneset, about five minutes by car from Stavanger city centre. It was apparently the cohabit-ant's flat. Kjetil is known to have worked with the sale and assembly of awnings. He was hired by 'Lars,' who was believed to be the cohabitant's younger brother. They had tapped into a big market for motorised terrace-awnings. However everything changed following a tax audit in spring 2014. Lars faced going to prison for tax evasion. Kjetil was himself at risk of prosecution because he had received benefits from the employment office throughout that period. He says they went on a bonding-trip to a trout lake, but they had not discussed anything worth mentioning. Kjetil believes he may still be suffering from derealisation when meeting other people. He also recalls that Lars had worn waders and had stood far out in the water while fishing. Lars supposedly had a quarter bottle of whiskey in his breast pocket. After a while his mood improved and he shouted to Kjetil that he should not worry. That evening they cooked two steaks on a disposable barbecue. Lars apparently sat and smoked cigarettes, Kjetil had no idea what his companion was thinking. Later on they went to sleep in their own little tents. Kjetil says that his thoughts were constantly restless. He felt no bond with the cohabitant and her three children, and was looking for a way out. He describes being anxious that he might behave violently. It is known that he slept badly that night. Kjetil says he went out to go to the toilet, he stood a short distance from the tent and urinated in the heather. It was still dark. He remembers birds moving around, out on the dark water.

The last few winters have been mild, with little or no snow in Stavanger. Winter 2014-15 was totally snow free. Kjetil Tuestad says he shovelled snow from the basement steps. It is unclear when this may have taken place. Here he describes sparklingly cold winter weather. He also feels that this recollection brings about anxiety. The snow-shovel had apparently scraped loudly on the steps. Kjetil says it was dark outside, it may have been early evening. He could hear kids sledging on the hill. Down by the main road, a clanking noise could be heard from some kind of vehicle with a chain. These were sounds to which he afforded meaning. Kjetil also describes the sound of shingle when he swept the backyard, small metallic particles, in otherwise deep, powdery snow.

Kjetil Tuestad talks about the loss of his own personality. He cannot recall being in touch with his own inner life. Kjetil thought a great deal about unreasonable situations, even assaults against himself. He could feel anger at that point. Sometimes he experienced difficulties in regulating his behaviour and emotions. It is understood that he paid a visit to a fellow patient from the Division of Psychiatry. She apparently lived at Storhaug. Kjetil walked several times along the snowy road. It had been a few years, she had bleached her hair and put on weight. Kjetil says the apartment was being done up. Half the lounge appeared to be sealed off with plastic. Kjetil says they stood in the middle of the floor. They had stood in silence. Kjetil does not think he could make out any of the renovation work, the materials and other things were supposedly obscured by the plastic. Kjetil had a vague sense of discomfort the whole time. He believes this discomfort was crucial to how he later remembered the episode. She had asked what he actually wanted. Kjetil said he did not know. Today he cannot recall what they were talking about. He thinks they may not have said a word. Kjetil Tuestad expresses difficulty in visualising himself in the situation. Kjetil says he was perhaps looking for something. It is believed they had sex in the woman's bedroom. The intercourse presumably took place late

in the afternoon. It had gradually become dark. Kjetil
found the woman to be listless, as in reluctant. He
has difficulty describing the face. He says the room
smelled of paint.

In autumn 2014, there was a fall in international crude oil prices. They would continue to drop throughout the following year. The petroleum industry sounded the alarm. It was presented as a state of global overproduction. Oil companies announced extensive cost cutting measures. Investments on the Norwegian continental shelf ended. All the major players experienced restructuring. The downsizing affected subcontractors in Stavanger and the neighbouring areas. Unemployment increased. Many feared that the country was on its way into a new recession.

It is known that Kjetil Tuestad disliked being unemployed. The days were long, it supposedly made him restless. He passed the time at the library. Sometimes he went and drank coffee at various shopping centres. He had moved into his own place, described as a small apartment behind the municipal housing blocks in Tjensvoll. Kjetil had noticeably thinner hair at this point. After a while he had cut it very short and was in effect bald. He had also started wearing glasses.

There are isolated incidents. It is known that Kjetil Tuestad often went to a disco at the weekends. He had supposedly tried amphetamines and developed a clear dependency on it. He recalls standing at a urinal and listening to bass rhythms from electronic dance music. He did not recognise himself. Kjetil is known to have spent a lot of time on the dance floor. He thinks it may have had something to do with challenging his own social phobias. During the period, he also found himself to be less self-critical. On isolated occasions he would go home with people in taxi. He talks about parties, it was a debauched life. Kjetil was eventually refused entry to the nightclub after he supposedly argued with the doormen. He thinks many could have found it strange. Most of them must have been significantly younger than him. Kjetil Tuestad recalls sharing a taxi with a highly inebriated woman, maybe in her late twenties. She had vomited in the bathroom apparently, and then lain there comatose. It was a very modern apartment. Kjetil says he had tried to make a cup of espresso. The time was by then half past two in the morning, he did not feel at all tired. He checked in on the woman curled up by the toilet bowl. He spread butter on a slice of bread and sat down in the woman's kitchen. But he did not feel hungry. A small Chihuahua scampered restlessly around the flat. He let the dog out into the garden, where it relieved itself on the grass. It was still dark outside. Kjetil had then returned to the bathroom. The woman had changed her position, her head and upper body were now lying across the floor. Kjetil says there was a noticeable amount of heat coming from the floor tiles. He crouched down and touched the woman's face gently. Kjetil recalls parting her lips, exposing her teeth and gums. He also touched the hair a little. Following that he went into the kitchen. Kjetil no longer had any clear idea of what he wanted. He doesn't recall having any thoughts. It is believed he looked in the fridge again. He gave the dog various cold meats and some ready-sliced cheese. Kjetil says he later went out into the dawn. He was allegedly in Eiganes, close to Stavanger stadium. He followed a chicken-wire fence through the housing estate. He saw no other people apparently. It may have been Sunday. A light dusk rain had settled on the artificial turf and the surrounding housing area.

It is known that the use of amphetamines had an increasing effect on Kjetil Tuestad's life. He had also entered a relationship with a single mother from Kristiansand during this period. He would usually sleep there every other weekend, when the children were out of the house. On isolated occasions he had complained of a relentless stream of thoughts. It is understood that it occasionally affected his sex life, and that Kjetil sometimes failed to get an erection. Kjetil believes he was about to lose his mind. He had woken the woman up in the middle of the night, she had then sat up in bed and was terrified. Kjetil says he laughed about this later. In reality he was worried. There had been constantly shifting thoughts, of a random and unfocussed nature. He had supposedly tried to quit during the autumn. There was a relapse. Kjetil celebrated Christmas 2015 with the parents in Madla. He had picked disinterestedly at the lamb ribs. The mother urged Kjetil to call his ex-wife in Hommersåk, which he did. There was a short conversation. He wished Ann Elisabet a Merry Christmas at least, the son would not come to the phone. The son was now in puberty. Ann Elisabet said that he was like his father in many ways. Kjetil had then gone into his parents' living room. They watched a movie on television. After the movie Kjetil had walked home to Tjensvoll. Kjetil is said to have lain down in the shower and urinated over his chest and neck. It has been said that in extreme situations he perceived urine as calming. He flicked between different movies on TV. During the evening Kjetil is said to have repeatedly sought sexual gratification by choking himself with his own belt. He turned off the TV. Then he took two sleeping pills. On Christmas Day he slept for several hours longer than usual. He allegedly mixed a bag of freeze-dried risotto with some water for breakfast. Kjetil was at that point hungry. During the day he also ate several hot-dogs at a 24-hour petrol station.